Ages 6-7
Key Stage 1

Supports the National Curriculum Key Stage 1

Times Tables

Bath · New York · Singapore · Hong Kong · Cologne · Delhi
Melbourne · Amsterdam · Johannesburg · Auckland · Shenzhen

Written by David Glover and Nina Filipek
Educational Consultant: Martin Malcolm
Illustrated by Simon Abbot

This edition published by Parragon in 2012

Parragon
Queen Street House
4 Queen Street
BATH, BA1 1HE, UK
www.parragon.com

ISBN 978-1-4454-7762-6

Printed in China

Helping your child

 Try to find a quiet place to work.

 Stop before your child grows tired and finish the page another time.

 Work through the pages in the right order – they get more difficult as you go on.

 Always give your child lots of encouragement and praise.

 The answers to the activities begin on page 121.

Contents

Contents

Understanding x2

Multiplication is like adding the same number many times.

2 x 2 is the same as 2 + 2

● ● + ● ● = ● ● ● ●

3 x 2 is the same as 2 + 2 + 2

● ●
● ●
● ●

Total = 6

Fill in the gaps.

4 x 2 is the same as

2 + ___ + 2 + ___

Total = ☐

5 x 2 is the same as

2 + ___ + 2 + ___ + 2

Total = ☐

6 x 2 is the same as

2 + ___ + 2 + ___ + 2 + ___

Total = ☐

Write the answers. Colour the ones you know by heart.

1 x **2** = ☐   2 x **2** = ☐

3 x **2** = ☐   4 x **2** = ☐

5 x **2** = ☐   6 x **2** = ☐

7 x **2** = ☐   8 x **2** = ☐

9 x **2** = ☐   10 x **2** = ☐

2 x 1 = ☐   2 x 2 = ☐

2 x 3 = ☐   2 x 4 = ☐

2 x 5 = ☐   2 x 6 = ☐

2 x 7 = ☐   2 x 8 = ☐

2 x 9 = ☐   2 x 10 = ☐

Write the missing numbers.

Two times table

Draw circles to put the fish in groups of two. Fill in the boxes.

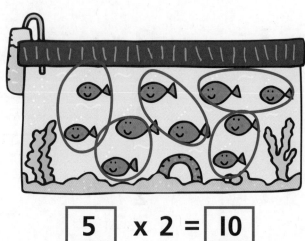

$$\boxed{5} \quad x \; 2 = \boxed{10}$$

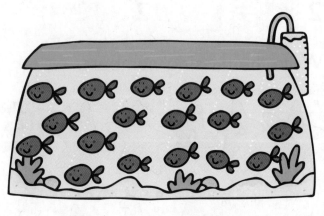

$$\boxed{} \quad x \; 2 = \boxed{}$$

[ ] x 2 = [ ]

[ ] x 2 = [ ]

Join each fish to its bowl.

10   1 x 2   12   8 x 2

5 x 2   4   6   2 x 2

2   3 x 2   16   6 x 2

Use your 2 times table to do these mental maths problems.

1. If a rabbit eats 2 carrots, then 2 rabbits will eat 4 carrots altogether.

2. If an octopus has 8 legs, how many legs will 2 octopuses have?

3. If one car seats 5 people, then 2 cars will seat ☐ people altogether.

4. If Jack has 3 points and Jill doubles his score, how many points does Jill have?

Jill has ☐ points

5. If 2 dogs eat 10 bones in 1 week, in 2 weeks they will eat ☐ bones altogether.

Complete these multiplications.

2 x 3 is the same as 3 x 2 and 3 + 3

Total = 6

3 x 3 is the same as

3 + 3 + ___

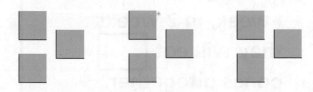

Total =

4 x 3 is the same as 3 x 4 and

4 + _____ + 4

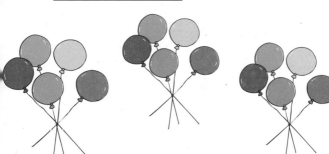

Total = ☐

5 x 3 is the same as 3 x 5 and

5 + _____

Total = ☐

Write the answers. Colour the
ones you know by heart.

1 x 3 = ☐

2 x 3 = ☐

3 x 3 = ☐

4 x 3 = ☐

5 x 3 = ☐

6 x 3 = ☐

7 x 3 = ☐

8 x 3 = ☐

9 x 3 = ☐

10 x 3 = ☐

3

15

3 x 1 = ☐

3 x 2 = ☐

3 x 3 = ☐

3 x 4 = ☐

3 x 5 = ☐

3 x 6 = ☐

3 x 7 = ☐

3 x 8 = ☐

3 x 9 = ☐

3 x 10 = ☐

Write the missing numbers.

18   27

Write the answers in the boxes.

3 x 5 = 15   5 x 3 =

7 x 3 =   3 x 7 =

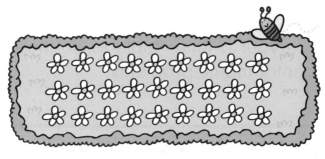

9 x 3 = ☐ 3 x 9 = ☐

Write the missing numbers.

8 x 3 = 24

4 x 3 =

9 x 3 =

3 x 🐌 = 15   3 🍃 x 3 = 9

7 x 🍃 = 21   🐌 x 3 = 18

🐌 x 3 = 30   3 x 🍃 = 6

Use your 3 times table to do these mental maths problems.

1. **How many corners do 2 triangles have altogether?**

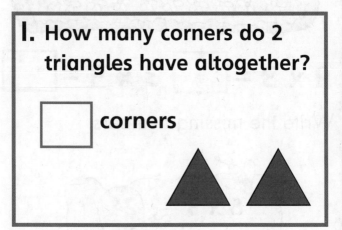

| | corners

2. **How many days in 3 weeks?**

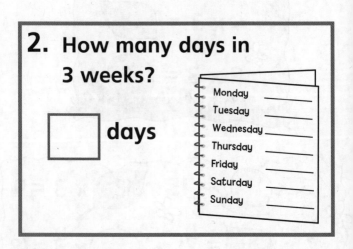

| | days

3. How many juggling balls do 3 clowns with 3 balls each have altogether?

[ ] balls

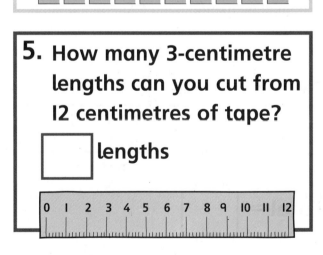

4. How many threes in 30?

[ ] threes in 30

5. How many 3-centimetre lengths can you cut from 12 centimetres of tape?

[ ] lengths

Understanding x4

Fill in the numbers. Draw the pictures too.

2 x 4 is the same as 4 x 2 and 4 + 4

Total = 8

3 x 4 is the same as 4 x 3 and

4 + 4 + ___

Total =

4 x 4 is the same as

4 + ___ + 4 + ___

Total =

5 x 4 is the same as 4 x 5 and

4 + _____

Total =

Write the answers. Colour the
ones you know by heart.

1 x 4 =

2 x 4 =

3 x 4 =

4 x 4 =

5 x 4 =

6 x 4 =

7 x 4 =

8 x 4 =

9 x 4 =

10 x 4 =

4 x 1 = ☐

4 x 2 = ☐

4 x 3 = ☐

4 x 4 = ☐

4 x 5 = ☐

4 x 6 = ☐

4 x 7 = ☐

4 x 8 = ☐

4 x 9 = ☐

4 x 10 = ☐

Write the missing numbers.

Four times table

Get the mouse to the cheese by colouring numbers in the four times table.

Start

2	14	12	4	8
5	40	24	16	20
24	36	6	10	18
32	41	23	19	21
4	16	5	45	26
25	20	17	1	13
34	8	10	22	35
11	12	29	15	3
19	28	7	30	27
31	40	16	20	12
33	6	32	4	36
2	30	7	35	24
16	8	14	9	8
40	24	12	40	16
4	45	28	32	7
12	3	21	11	5
20	37	17	21	41
28	9	15	42	25

Finish

Join each cat to a ball of wool.

3 x 4	8
10 x 4	24
4 x 4	12
6 x 4	28
5 x 4	40
2 x 4	16
7 x 4	20

Use your 4 times table to do these mental maths problems.

I. What do 4 lots of 4 make?

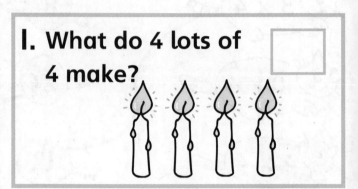

2. Multiply 4 by 3.

3. Four times 5 is

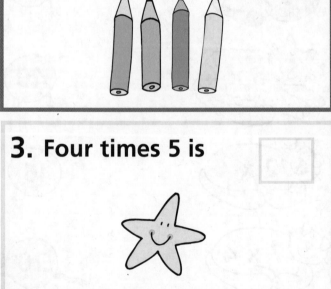

4. How many corners do 2 squares have altogether?

5. How many fours in 20?

6. How many legs do 6 horses have altogether?

Fill in the boxes:

X	3	2	4
5	15		
6			
8			

X	4	9	7
4			
2			
3			

Jump in twos

0 1 ② 3 ④ 5 6 7 8 9 10

11 12 13 14 15 16 17 18 19 20

Jump in threes

0 1 2 ③ 4 5 6 7 8 9 10

11 12 13 14 15 16 17 18 19 20

Jump in fours

0 1 2 3 ④ 5 6 7 8 9 10

11 12 13 14 15 16 17 18 19 20

What does each set of
clothes cost?

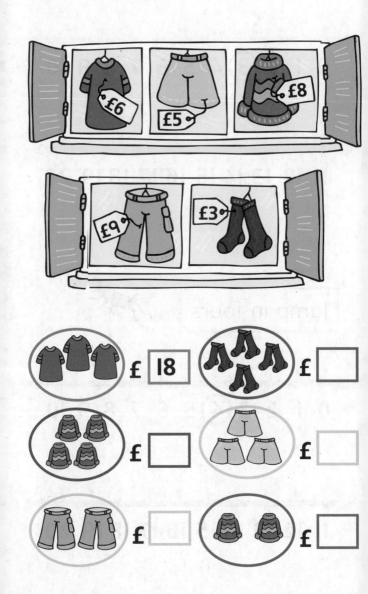

How fast can you
answer these questions?
Time yourself!

5 x 2 = ☐   10 x 3 = ☐

9 x 3 = ☐   2 x 4 = ☐

4 x 6 = ☐   4 x 10 = ☐

2 x 7 = ☐   6 x 3 = ☐

8 x 3 = ☐   2 x 2 = ☐

4 x 5 = ☐   2 x 4 = ☐

9 x 2 = ☐   4 x 7 = ☐

3 x 3 = ☐   4 x 3 = ☐

Multiplication machines

Write the missing numbers coming out of the machine.

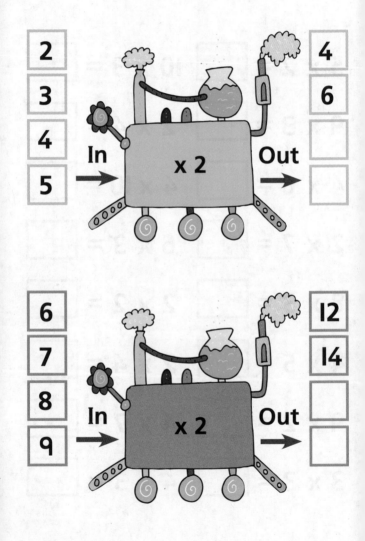

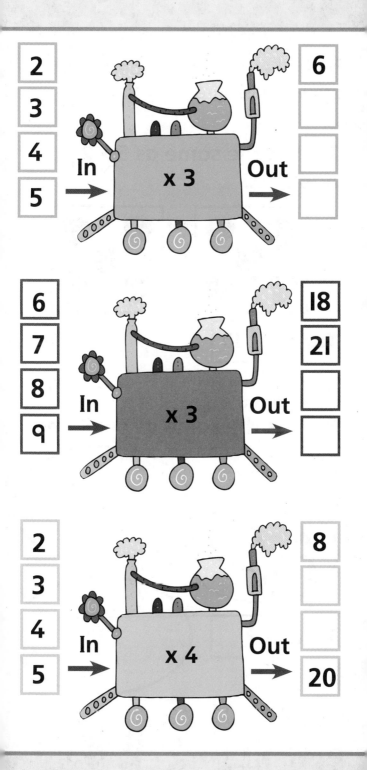

2
3
4
5

In → x 3 → Out

6

6
7
8
9

In → x 3 → Out

18
21

2
3
4
5

In → x 4 → Out

8

20

Put in the missing numbers and draw the pictures.

2 x 5 is the same as 5 x 2 and 5 + 5

Total = | 10 |

3 x 5 is the same as 5 x 3 and 5 + 5 + ___

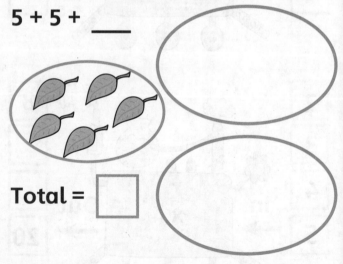

Total = [ ]

5 x 5 is the same as

5 + _____

Total =

7 x 5 is the same as 5 x 7 and

5 + _____

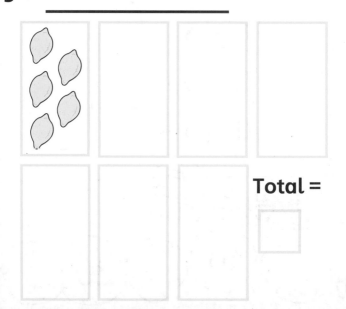

Total =

Write the answers. Colour the ones you know by heart.

$1 \times 5 =$ ☐

$2 \times 5 =$ ☐

$3 \times 5 =$ ☐

$4 \times 5 =$ ☐

$5 \times 5 =$ ☐

$6 \times 5 =$ ☐

$7 \times 5 =$ ☐

$8 \times 5 =$ ☐

$9 \times 5 =$ ☐

$10 \times 5 =$ ☐

10   20

$5 \times 1 =$ ☐

$5 \times 2 =$ ☐

$5 \times 3 =$ ☐

$5 \times 4 =$ ☐

$5 \times 5 =$ ☐

$5 \times 6 =$ ☐

$5 \times 7 =$ ☐

$5 \times 8 =$ ☐

$5 \times 9 =$ ☐

$5 \times 10 =$ ☐

Write the missing numbers.

35 **40**

Five times table

Colour the squares with numbers from the five times table.

15	5	45	30	15
14	22	5	18	20
56	12	10	16	25
22	27	39	41	32
10	15	40	50	35
16	2	8	34	17
42	34	21	30	45
9	5	25	27	41
20	38	46	21	36
13	35	50	18	12
28	21	7	40	5
34	29	48	34	26
35	20	5	45	15
30	18	50	31	30
40	9	10	3	25

Now turn the book on its side. Which number can you see? _____

Write the missing numbers.

⬭ x 5 = 30

5 x ☕ = 15

🍵 x 5 = 5

10 x 5 = 🍽

☕ x 5 = 45

8 x 5 = 🍵

☕ x 5 = 10

5 x ☕ = 25

🍽 x 5 = 20

5 x ☕ = 35

Use your 5 times table to do these mental maths problems.

1. If there are 5 pencils in a box, how many pencils are in 5 boxes?

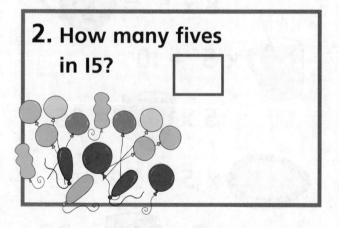

2. How many fives in 15?

3. If Matt is 5 years old and his brother, Tom, is twice his age, how old is Tom?

4. A pentagon has 5 sides. How many sides do 4 pentagons have altogether?

5. What is 5 x 2 x 5?

Put in the missing numbers and draw the pictures.

2 x 6 is the same as 6 x 2 and 6 + 6

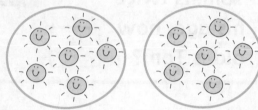

Total = 12

3 x 6 is the same as 6 x 3 and 6 + _____

Total = ☐

5 x 6 is the same as 6 x 5 and

6 + _____

Total =

[ ]

6 x 6 is the same as

6 + _____

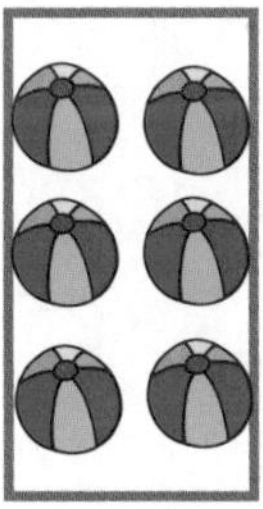

Total = [ ]

Six times table

Write the answers. Colour the ones you know by heart.

1 x 6 = ☐

2 x 6 = ☐

3 x 6 = ☐

4 x 6 = ☐

5 x 6 = ☐

6 x 6 = ☐

7 x 6 = ☐

8 x 6 = ☐

9 x 6 = ☐

10 x 6 = ☐

6   24   30

6 x 1 = ☐

6 x 2 = ☐

6 x 3 = ☐

6 x 4 = ☐

6 x 5 = ☐

6 x 6 = ☐

6 x 7 = ☐

6 x 8 = ☐

6 x 9 = ☐

6 x 10 = ☐

Write the missing numbers.

Six times table

Write the answers to the 6 times table in words.

10 x 6 = _ _ _ _ _ _

5 x 6 = _ _ _ _ _ _

3 x 6 = _ _ _ _ _ _ _ _

8 x 6 = _ _ _ _ _ - _ _ _ _ _

6 x 6 = _ _ _ _ _ _ - _ _ _

7 x 6 = _ _ _ _ _ - _ _ _

2 x 6 = _ _ _ _ _ _

1 x 6 = _ _ _

Fit all your answers into
this puzzle.

t w e n t y f o u r

Use your 6 times table to do these mental maths problems.

1. If a window cleaner can clean 6 windows in half an hour, how many can he clean in one hour? ☐

2. If a bunch of flowers costs £6, how much do 3 bunches cost?

£ ☐

3. If the red team scores 6 points and the blue team scores 4 times this, how many points does the blue team score?

☐

4. If an insect has 6 legs, how many legs do 5 insects have altogether?

☐

5. If a snail crawls 6 centimetres in 5 minutes, how far does it crawl in 10 minutes?

☐

Put in the missing numbers and draw the pictures.

2 x 7 is the same as 7 x 2 and 7 + 7

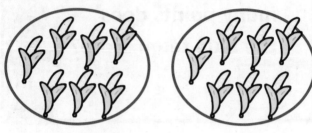

Total = 14

3 x 7 is the same as 7 x 3 and

7 + _____

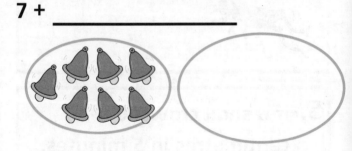

Total =

6 x 7 is the same as 7 x 6 and _____

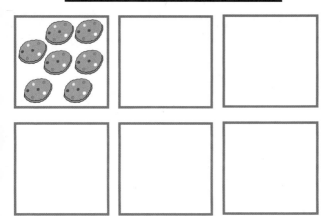

Total = ☐

7 x 7 is the same as

_____

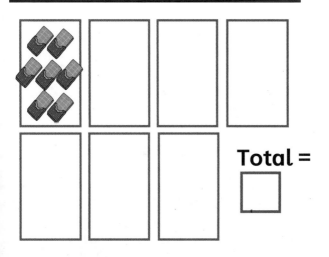

Total = ☐

Seven times table

Write the answers. Colour the ones you know by heart.

1 x 7 = ☐

2 x 7 = ☐

3 x 7 = ☐

4 x 7 = ☐

5 x 7 = ☐

6 x 7 = ☐

7 x 7 = ☐

8 x 7 = ☐

9 x 7 = ☐

10 x 7 = ☐

21

28

7 x 1 = ☐

7 x 2 = ☐

7 x 3 = ☐

7 x 4 = ☐

7 x 5 = ☐

7 x 6 = ☐

7 x 7 = ☐

7 x 8 = ☐

7 x 9 = ☐

7 x 10 = ☐

Write the missing numbers.

49   63

Seven times table

Join each cloud to a sun or moon.

Get the bees through the maze
by colouring numbers in the
7 times table.

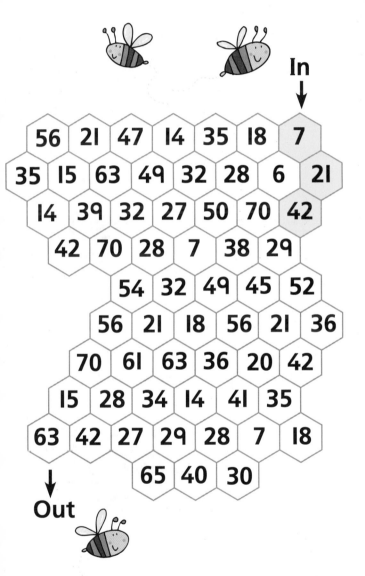

Mental maths x7

Use your 7 times table to do these mental maths problems.

1. If I eat I apple every day for 2 weeks, how many apples have I eaten altogether?

[ ] apples

2. If the train fare is £7 a day, how much is the fare for 5 days in total?

£ [ ]

3. If 7 children came to my party and they each drank 3 glasses of orange juice, how many glasses in total would they drink?

☐ glasses

4. If I'm 7 years old and my grandma is 10 times older, how old is my grandma?

☐ years old

5. There are 7 bananas in a bunch. I buy 4 bunches. How many bananas do I have altogether?

☐ bananas

Learn the facts

Fill in the boxes.

X	6	7	5
8			
3			15
9			

X	6		
5			35
7		28	
6			

Join each kite to a tree. Draw a circle around the tree with the most kites tied to it.

4 x 5

6 x 6

6 x 4

7 x 7

7 x 4

7 x 6

8 x 5

9 x 5

8 x 6

5 x 7

6 x 5

Answers that start with 2

Answers that start with 3

Answers that start with 4

Use the clues to fill in the puzzle.

1 **4**	**2**	2	3	
1 **9**	4		5	6
7		8	9	
	10			11
12		13	14	

Across
1. 6 x 7
3. 7 x 2
4. 9 x 6
5. 3 x 7
7. 6 x 5
9. 5 x 9
10. 8 x 5
12. 5 x 5
13. 1 x 7
14. 6 x 3

Down
1. 7 x 7
2. 6 x 4
3. 2 x 6
4. 10 x 5
6. 3 x 5
7. 6 x 6
8. 7 x 10
9. 7 x 6
10. 9 x 5
11. 4 x 7

How fast can you answer
these questions?
Time yourself!

1. 5 x 4 = ☐   6 x 7 = ☐

2. 9 x 6 = ☐   7 x 10 = ☐

3. 7 x 2 = ☐   2 x 6 = ☐

4. 6 x 5 = ☐   5 x 5 = ☐

5. 7 x 7 = ☐   7 x 5 = ☐

6. 6 x 6 = ☐   6 x 10 = ☐

7. 8 x 5 = ☐   5 x 9 = ☐

8. 9 x 7 = ☐

Robot revision

These robots have forgotten their times tables. They need your help! Tell them which answers are wrong. Write the correct answers for them.

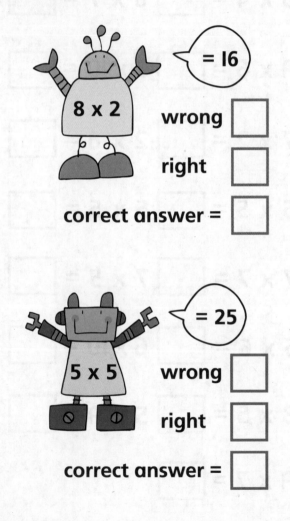

= 16

8 x 2

wrong ☐

right ☐

correct answer = ☐

= 25

5 x 5

wrong ☐

right ☐

correct answer = ☐

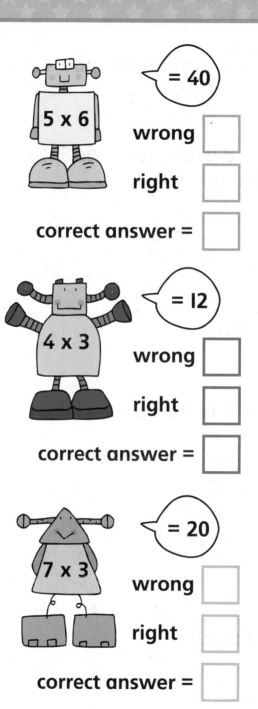

5 x 6   = 40

wrong ☐

right ☐

correct answer = ☐

4 x 3   = 12

wrong ☐

right ☐

correct answer = ☐

7 x 3   = 20

wrong ☐

right ☐

correct answer = ☐

Put in the missing numbers and draw the pictures.

2 x 8 is the same as 8 x 2 and 8 + 8

Total = ☐

4 x 8 is the same as 8 x 4 and 8 + _____

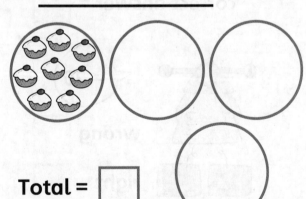

Total = ☐

6 x 8 is the same as 8 x 6 and

_____

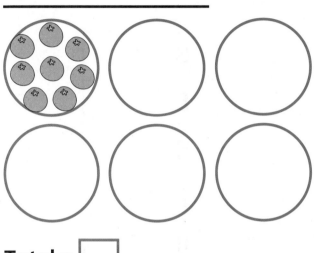

Total = ☐

7 x 8 is the same as 8 x 7 and

_____

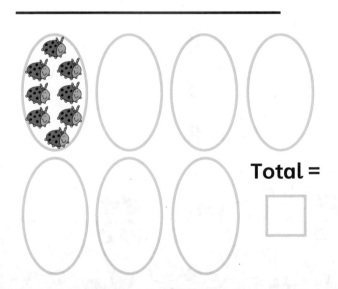

Total =

☐

Write the answers. Colour the ones you know by heart.

1 x 8 =

2 x 8 =

3 x 8 =

4 x 8 =

5 x 8 =

6 x 8 =

7 x 8 =

8 x 8 =

9 x 8 =

10 x 8 =

8 x 1 = ☐

8 x 2 = ☐

8 x 3 = ☐

8 x 4 = ☐

8 x 5 = ☐

8 x 6 = ☐

8 x 7 = ☐

8 x 8 = ☐

8 x 9 = ☐

8 x 10 = ☐

Write the missing numbers.

Eight times table

Join each shell to a dolphin.

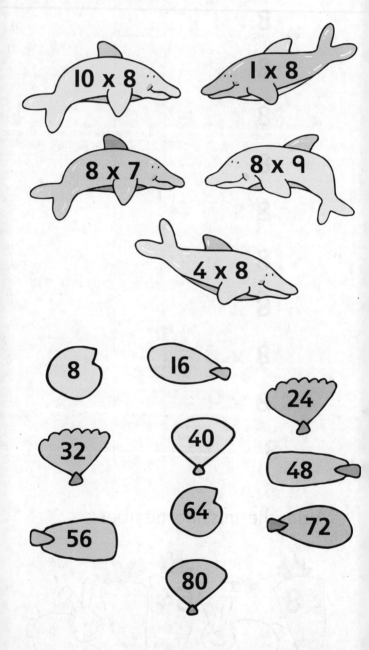

Write the missing numbers.

 x 8 = 24

8 x = 40

 x 6 = 48

7 x 8 =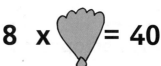

9 x  = 72

2 x 8 =

 x 10 = 80

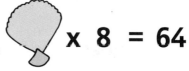 x 8 = 64

4 x = 32

Mental maths x8

Use your 8 times table to do these mental maths problems.

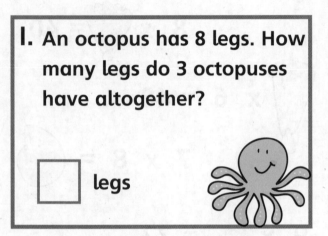

1. An octopus has 8 legs. How many legs do 3 octopuses have altogether?

☐ legs

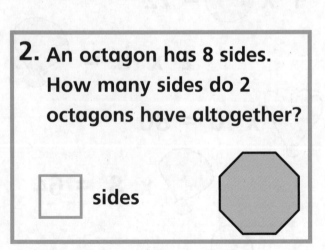

2. An octagon has 8 sides. How many sides do 2 octagons have altogether?

☐ sides

3. What is 4 times 8 or 8 times 4?

◯ ◯ ◯ ◯

☐

4. How many eights make 40?

☐

5. A journey takes 8 hours by plane, but 10 times longer by car. How long does the car journey take?

☐ hours

Put in the missing numbers and draw the pictures.

2 x 9 is the same as 9 x 2 and 9 + 9

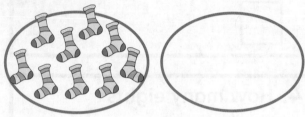

Total = ☐

4 x 9 is the same as 9 x 4 and

_____

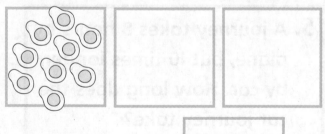

Total = ☐   ☐

5 x 9 is the same as 9 x 5 and

_____

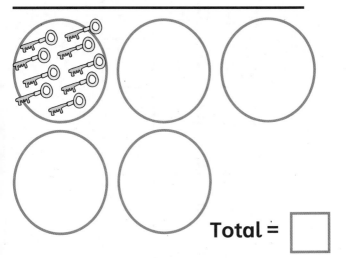

Total = ☐

9 x 9 is the same as

_____

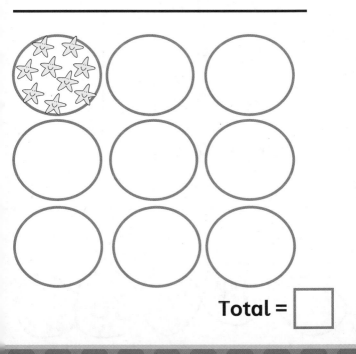

Total = ☐

Write the answers. Colour the ones you know by heart.

1 x 9 = ☐

2 x 9 = ☐

3 x 9 = ☐

4 x 9 = ☐

5 x 9 = ☐

6 x 9 = ☐

7 x 9 = ☐

8 x 9 = ☐

9 x 9 = ☐

10 x 9 = ☐

9 x 1 = ☐

9 x 2 = ☐

9 x 3 = ☐

9 x 4 = ☐

9 x 5 = ☐

9 x 6 = ☐

9 x 7 = ☐

9 x 8 = ☐

9 x 9 = ☐

9 x 10 = ☐

Write the missing numbers.

63

Answer these.

$3 \times 9 =$ ☐

$8 \times 9 =$ ☐

$2 \times 9 =$ ☐

$9 \times 9 =$ ☐

$1 \times 9 =$ ☐

$6 \times 9 =$ ☐

$5 \times 9 =$ ☐

$4 \times 9 =$ ☐

$7 \times 9 =$ ☐

$10 \times 9 =$ ☐

Colour in the numbers from the nine times table.

Which letter of the alphabet can you see?

Use your 9 times table to do these mental maths problems.

I. What is double nine?

2. What are three nines?

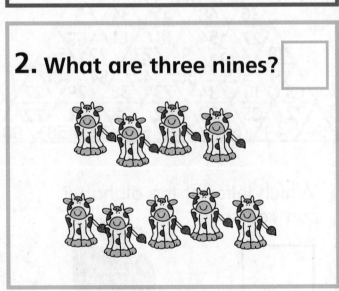

3. How many nines in thirty-six?

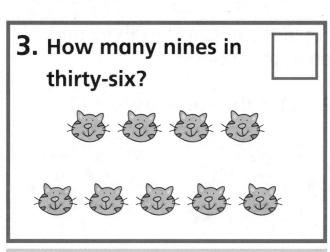

4. What is 5 x 9 or 9 x 5?

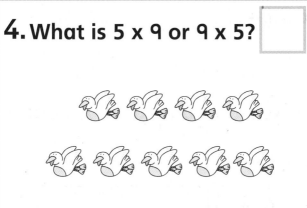

5. How many nines in eighty-one?

Put in the missing numbers and draw the pictures.

2 x 10 is the same as 10 + 10

Total = ☐

4 x 10 is the same as 10 x 4 and

_____

 ☐ ☐

Total = ☐ ☐

6 x 10 is the same as 10 x 6 and

_____

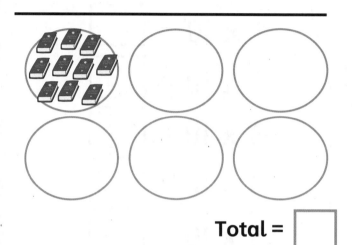

Total = ☐

10 x 10 is the same as

_____

Total = ☐

Ten times table

Write the answers. Colour the ones you know by heart.

1 x 10 = ☐

2 x 10 = ☐

3 x 10 = ☐

4 x 10 = ☐

5 x 10 = ☐

6 x 10 = ☐

7 x 10 = ☐

8 x 10 = ☐

9 x 10 = ☐

10 x 10 = ☐

10 x 1 =

10 x 2 =

10 x 3 =

10 x 4 =

10 x 5 =

10 x 6 =

10 x 7 =

10 x 8 =

10 x 9 =

10 x 10 =

Write the missing numbers.

60   80

Find a path through the maze by circling the numbers from the ten times table.

↓ In

(40)	70	20	18	32	45	12
35	42	50	21	61	34	18
60	30	90	22	30	60	100
20	92	18	48	90	92	20
100	40	80	70	10	85	70
72	55	41	3	8	36	30
50	100	90	87	80	90	50
10	29	30	46	10	62	94
(80)	74	60	40	20	42	38

↓ Out

Write the missing numbers.

◯ x 10 = 100

9 x 10 = ◯

◯ x 6 = 60

8 x ◯ = 80

◯ x 10 = 70

5 x 10 = ◯

10 x ◯ = 20

10 x ◯ = 40

10 x ◯ = 30

Use your 10 times table to do these mental maths problems.

1. 10 children are at a party. They eat 2 jellies each. How many jellies do they eat in total? ☐

2. How many 10-centimetre lengths can you cut from 30 centimetres of tape? ☐

3. A little monster weighs 10 kilos and a big monster weighs 10 times more. What is the weight of the big monster?

☐

4. It takes me 1 hour to walk 1 mile. How long will it take me to walk 10 miles?

☐

5. If a balloon costs 5p, how much will it cost to buy 10 balloons?

☐

Fill in the puzzles.

X	9	10	5
3			
7			
6			

X	6		
9			72
8		40	
10	60		

Write the missing numbers going in and coming out of the machine.

In	× 9	Out
4		
		72
9		
		18
7		
		45

In	× 10	Out
3		
		40
8		
		60
5		
		90

Learn the facts

Write the clues to match
the answers.

1. 8	0	2. 1	3. 2	0
1	4. 4	8	5. 4	6. 5
7. 6	0	8. 7	9. 1	0
3	10. 3	2	6	11. 3
12. 9	0	13. 9	14. 5	6

Across		Down	
1. ☐ X ☐		1. ☐ X ☐	
3. ☐ X ☐		2. ☐ X ☐	
4. ☐ X ☐		3. ☐ X ☐	
5. ☐ X ☐		4. ☐ X ☐	
7. ☐ X ☐		6. ☐ X ☐	
9. ☐ X ☐		7. ☐ X ☐	
10. ☐ X ☐		8. ☐ X ☐	
12. ☐ X ☐		9. ☐ X ☐	
13. ☐ X ☐		10. ☐ X ☐	
14. ☐ X ☐		11. ☐ X ☐	

How fast can you answer
these questions?
Time yourself!

1. $4 \times 9 =$ ☐ $5 \times 9 =$ ☐

2. $10 \times 5 =$ ☐ $6 \times 8 =$ ☐

3. $8 \times 9 =$ ☐ $10 \times 8 =$ ☐

4. $9 \times 2 =$ ☐ $3 \times 10 =$ ☐

5. $3 \times 8 =$ ☐ $8 \times 7 =$ ☐

6. $2 \times 8 =$ ☐ $8 \times 10 =$ ☐

7. $6 \times 9 =$ ☐ $9 \times 9 =$ ☐

8. $10 \times 2 =$ ☐

Looking for patterns

Finish the 2x pattern.
Then colour the answers for
the other times tables.

2x

1	2	3	4	5	6	7	8	9	10
11	12	13	14	15	16	17	18	19	20

3x

1	2	3	4	5	6	7	8	9	10
11	12	13	14	15	16	17	18	19	20
21	22	23	24	25	26	27	28	29	30

5x

1	2	3	4	5	6	7	8	9	10
11	12	13	14	15	16	17	18	19	20
21	22	23	24	25	26	27	28	29	30
31	32	33	34	35	36	37	38	39	40
41	42	43	44	45	46	47	48	49	50

Can you see the patterns?

9x

1	2	3	4	5	6	7	8	9	10
11	12	13	14	15	16	17	18	19	20
21	22	23	24	25	26	27	28	29	30
31	32	33	34	35	36	37	38	39	40
41	42	43	44	45	46	47	48	49	50
51	52	53	54	55	56	57	58	59	60
61	62	63	64	65	66	67	68	69	70
71	72	73	74	75	76	77	78	79	80
81	82	83	84	85	86	87	88	89	90

10x

1	2	3	4	5	6	7	8	9	10
11	12	13	14	15	16	17	18	19	20
21	22	23	24	25	26	27	28	29	30
31	32	33	34	35	36	37	38	39	40
41	42	43	44	45	46	47	48	49	50
51	52	53	54	55	56	57	58	59	60
61	62	63	64	65	66	67	68	69	70
71	72	73	74	75	76	77	78	79	80
81	82	83	84	85	86	87	88	89	90
91	92	93	94	95	96	97	98	99	100

Put in the missing numbers.

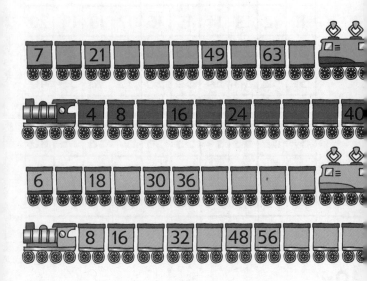

Multiply the number of columns by the number of rows.
3 columns x 2 rows = 6.

Row

Column

$3 \times 2 = 6$

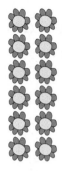 

$\boxed{} \times \boxed{} = \boxed{}$

$\boxed{} \times \boxed{} = \boxed{}$

All together

Do you know all your times tables?
Fill in the missing numbers.

x	1	2	3	4	5
1	1	2	3	4	5
2	2	4	6	8	10
3					
4					
5					
6					
7					
8					
9					
10					

x	6	7	8	9	10
1	6	7	8	9	10
2	12	14	16	18	20
3					
4					
5					
6					
7					
8					
9					
10					

All together

Fill in the missing numbers.

$4 \times 6 = \boxed{}$

$\boxed{} \times 8 = 24$

$7 \times 8 = \boxed{}$

$7 \times 9 = \boxed{}$

$7 \times \boxed{} = 42$

$9 \times \boxed{} = 72$

$\boxed{} \times 5 = 40$

$\boxed{} \times 7 = 35$

Which is bigger?

40

42

5 x 8   or   6 x 7

3 x 4   or   2 x 5

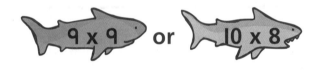

9 x 9   or   10 x 8

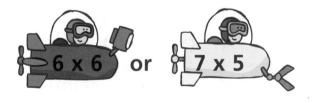

6 x 6   or   7 x 5

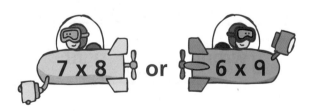

7 x 8   or   6 x 9

Put a tick by the right answers and a cross by the wrong ones.

$4 \times 2 = 8$

☐ wrong ☐ right

$2 \times 3 = 6$

☐ wrong ☐ right

$4 \times 3 = 14$

☐ wrong ☐ right

$4 \times 4 = 18$

☐ wrong ☐ right

$5 \times 3 = 53$

☐ wrong ☐ right

5 x 4 = 21

☐ wrong   ☐ right

6 x 5 = 30

☐ wrong   ☐ right

3 x 6 = 18

☐ wrong   ☐ right

4 x 6 = 24

☐ wrong   ☐ right

2 x 7 = 14

☐ wrong   ☐ right

7 x 7 = 49

☐ wrong   ☐ right

Multiplication squares

Fill in the missing numbers.

2	x	4	=	8
x	■	x	■	x
	x	1	=	
=	■	=	■	=
4	x		=	16

3	x	2	=	6
x	■	x	■	x
3	x		=	
=	■	=	■	=
9	x		=	18

3	x	1	=	
x	■	x	■	x
	x	2	=	8
=	■	=	■	=
12	x		=	24

	x	2	=	10
x	■	x	■	x
5	x		=	5
=	■	=	■	=
25	x	2	=	

Code breaker

This code uses numbers instead of letters. Fill in the blue boxes to find the secret message!

A	B	C	D	E	F
14	23	27	40	100	50
G	H	I	J	K	L
70	20	45	25	86	90

M	N	O	P	Q	R	S
24	11	34	49	17	36	16
T	U	V	W	X	Y	Z
9	18	21	26	60	83	92

Write the letters here to reveal the secret message:

__ __ __ __ __ __ __ __ __

6 x 4 = [ ] _____

7 x 2 = [ ] _____

3 x 3 = [9] __T__

4 x 5 = [ ] _____

8 x 2 = [ ] _____

9 x 5 = [ ] _____

4 x 4 = [ ] _____

2 x 7 = [ ] _____

9 x 3 = [27] __C__

10 x 10 = [ ] _____

Snakes and ladders

Multiply your starting number
until you get to the answer box.
Go down the snakes and up
the ladders!

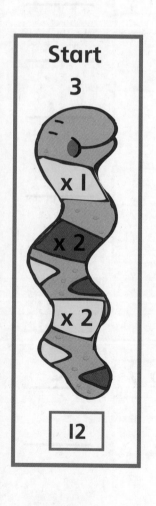

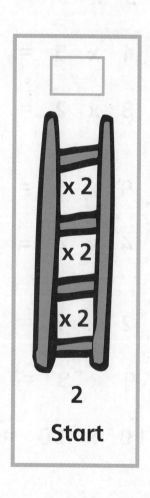

Start
5

x 1

x 2

x 5

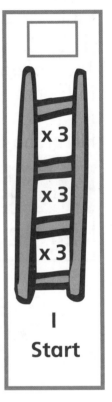

x 3

x 3

x 3

1
Start

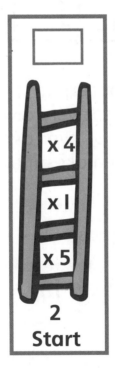

x 4

x 1

x 5

2
Start

Table Tricks

There's a pattern in the 4 times table. The answers always end: 4, 8, 2, 6, 0, over and over again. The pattern makes it easy to count in fours.

Fill in the gaps.

4	8	12	16	20
24_	2__	3__	3__	4__

There's a pattern in the 6 times table. The answers always end: 6, 2, 8, 4, 0, over and over again. The pattern makes it easy to count in sixes.

Fill in the gaps.

6	12	18	24	30
36_	4__	4__	5__	6__

There's a pattern in the 8 times table. The answers end by counting backwards in twos: 8, 6, 4, 2, 0. The pattern makes it easy to count in eights.

Fill in the gaps.

8	16	24	32	40
48	5_	6_	7_	8_

There's a pattern in the 9 times table. The answers end by counting backwards in ones: 9, 8, 7, 6, 5, 4, 3, 2 ,1, 0. The pattern makes it easy to count in nines.

Fill in the gaps.

9	18	27	3_	4_
54	6_	7_	8_	9_

Multiplying mates

Some answers turn up in lots of different times tables. Like this:

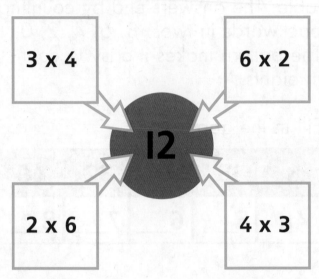

3 x 4	6 x 2

12

2 x 6	4 x 3

Fill in the blue boxes to match the red circle.

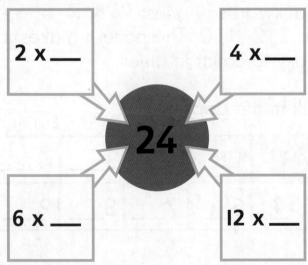

2 x ___	4 x ___

24

6 x ___	12 x ___

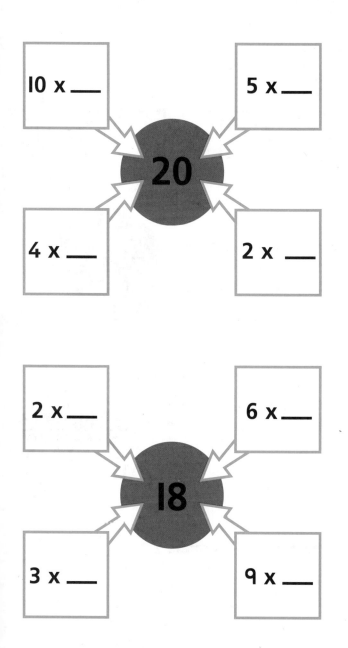

10 x ___

5 x ___

4 x ___

2 x ___

20

2 x ___

6 x ___

3 x ___

9 x ___

18

Fill the gaps

Fill in the missing numbers.

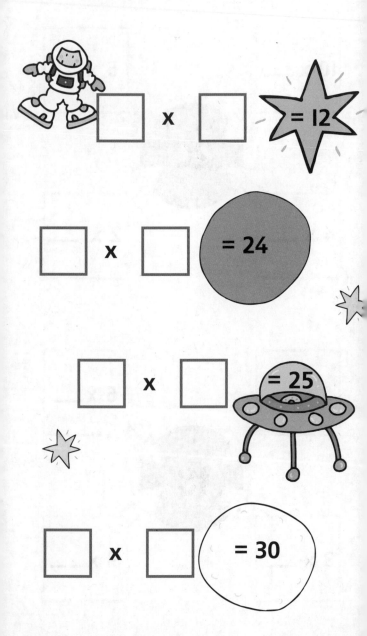

☐ x ☐ = 12

☐ x ☐ = 24

☐ x ☐ = 25

☐ x ☐ = 30

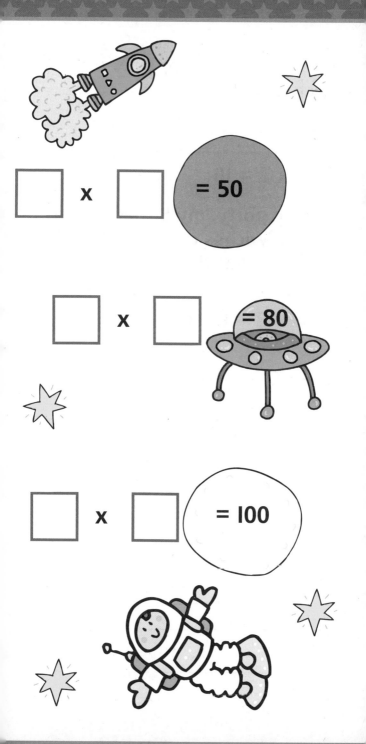

☐ x ☐ = 50

☐ x ☐ = 80

☐ x ☐ = 100

Number stories

Make up a number story for each multiplication.

$5 \times 2 = 10$

At my party, my 5 friends ate 2 sandwiches each. They ate 10 sandwiches altogether.

$4 \times 3 = 12$

_____

_____

_____

$6 \times 5 = 30$

_____

_____

_____

7 x 6 = 42

_____

_____

_____

8 x 9 = 72

_____

_____

_____

10 x 9 = 90

_____

_____

_____

Sorting hats

Circle the multiplication that matches the answer in the wizard's hat.

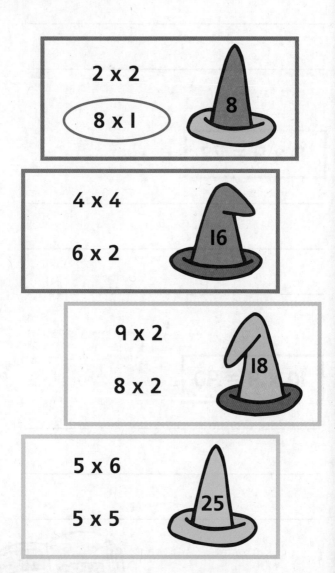

2 x 2

(8 x 1)

8

4 x 4

6 x 2

16

9 x 2

8 x 2

18

5 x 6

5 x 5

25

Answers

Pages 8–9 Understanding x2

4 x 2 is the same as 2 + 2 + 2 + 2 Total = 8
5 x 2 is the same as 2 + 2 + 2 + 2 + 2 Total = 10
6 x 2 is the same as 2 + 2 + 2 + 2 + 2 + 2 Total = 12

Pages 10–11 Two times table

1 x 2 = 2, 2 x 2 = 4, 3 x 2 = 6, 4 x 2 = 8, 5 x 2 = 10,
6 x 2 = 12, 7 x 2 = 14, 8 x 2 = 16, 9 x 2 = 18,
10 x 2 = 20   Missing numbers are: 8, 10, 14, 18, 20

Pages 12–13 Two times table

5 x 2 = 10, 9 x 2 = 18, 7 x 2 = 14, 6 x 2 = 12.
1 x 2 = 2, 8 x 2 = 16, 5 x 2 = 10, 2 x 2 = 4, 3 x 2 = 6,
6 x 2 = 12

Pages 14–15 Mental maths x2

1. 2 x 2 = 4 carrots 2. 8 x 2 or 2 x 8 = 16 legs
3. 5 x 2 or 2 x 5 = 10 people 4. 3 x 2 or 2 x 3 = 6 points
5. 2 x 10 or 10 x 2 = 20 bones

Pages 16–17 Understanding x3

3 x 3 is the same as 3 + 3 + 3 Total = 9
4 x 3 is the same as 4 + 4 + 4 Total = 12
5 x 3 is the same as 5 + 5 + 5 Total = 15

Pages 18–19 Three times table

1 x 3 = 3, 2 x 3 = 6, 3 x 3 = 9,
4 x 3 = 12, 5 x 3 = 15, 6 x 3 = 18, 7 x 3 = 21,
8 x 3 = 24, 9 x 3 = 27, 10 x 3 = 30
Missing numbers are: 6, 9, 12, 21, 24, 30

Pages 20–21 Three times table

3 x 5 = 15, 5 x 3 = 15, 7 x 3 = 21, 3 x 7 = 21,
9 x 3 = 27, 3 x 9 = 27
Missing numbers are: 8 x 3 = 24, 4 x 3 = 12, 9 x 3 = 27,
3 x 5 = 15, 3 x 3 = 9, 7 x 3 = 21, 6 x 3 = 18, 10 x 3 = 30,
3 x 2 = 6

Pages 22–23 Mental maths x3

1. 3 x 2 or 2 x 3 = 6 corners 2. 7 x 3 or 3 x 7 = 21 days
3. 3 x 3 = 9 balls 4. 10 threes in 30 5. 4 lengths

Pages 24–25 Understanding x4

3 x 4 is the same as 4 + 4 + 4 Total = 12
4 x 4 is the same as 4 + 4 + 4 + 4 Total = 16
5 x 4 is the same as 4 + 4 + 4 + 4 + 4 Total = 20

Answers

Pages 26–27 Four times table

1 x 4 = 4, 2 x 4 = 8, 3 x 4 = 12, 4 x 4 = 16, 5 x 4 = 20,
6 x 4 = 24, 7 x 4 = 28, 8 x 4 = 32, 9 x 4 = 36, 10 x 4 = 40
Missing numbers are: 4, 12, 24, 28, 36, 40

Pages 28–29 Four times table

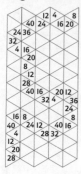

3 x 4 = 12, 10 x 4 = 40,
4 x 4 = 16, 6 x 4 = 24,
5 x 4 = 20, 2 x 4 = 8,
7 x 4 = 28

Pages 30–31 Mental maths x4

1. 4 x 4 = 16 2. 4 x 3 = 12 3. 4 x 5 = 20
4. 4 x 2 = 8 corners 5. 5 fours in 20 6. 4 x 6 = 24

Pages 32–33 Learn the facts

X	3	2	4
5	15	10	20
6	18	12	24
8	24	16	32

X	4	9	7
4	16	36	28
2	8	18	14
3	12	27	21

2x table 2, 4, 6, 8, 10, 12, 14, 16, 18, 20
3x table 3, 6, 9, 12, 15, 18
4x table 4, 8, 12, 16, 20

Pages 34–35 Learn the facts

Totals are: top row: £18, £12 middle row: £32, £15
bottom row: £18, £16
row 1: 10, 30 row 2: 27, 8 row 3: 24, 40
row 4: 14, 18 row 5: 24, 4 row 6: 20, 8
row 7: 18, 28 row 8: 9, 12

Pages 36–37 Multiplication machines

x2 machine	x2 machine	x3 machine
2 x 2 = 4	6 x 2 = 12	2 x 3 = 6
3 x 2 = 6	7 x 2 = 14	3 x 3 = 9
4 x 2 = 8	8 x 2 = 16	4 x 3 = 12
5 x 2 = 10	9 x 2 = 18	5 x 3 = 15

x3 machine	x4 machine
6 x 3 = 18	2 x 4 = 8
7 x 3 = 21	3 x 4 = 12
8 x 3 = 24	4 x 4 = 16
9 x 3 = 27	5 x 4 = 20

Pages 38–39 Understanding x5

2 x 5 is the same as 5 + 5 Total = 10
3 x 5 is the same as 5 + 5 + 5 Total = 15
5 x 5 is the same as 5 + 5 + 5 + 5 + 5 Total = 25
7 x 5 is the same as 5 + 5 + 5 + 5 + 5 + 5 + 5 Total = 35

Pages 40–41 Five times table

1 x 5 = 5, 2 x 5 = 10, 3 x 5 = 15, 4 x 5 = 20,
5 x 5 = 25, 6 x 5 = 30, 7 x 5 = 35, 8 x 5 = 40,
9 x 5 = 45, 10 x 5 = 50
Missing numbers are: 5, 15, 25, 30, 45, 50

Pages 42–43 Five times table

You can see the number FIVE in the grid.
6 x 5 = 30, 5 x 3 = 15, 1 x 5 = 5, 10 x 5 = 50, 9 x 5 = 45,
8 x 5 = 40, 2 x 5 = 10, 5 x 5 = 25, 4 x 5 = 20, 5 x 7 = 35

Pages 44–45 Mental maths x5

1. 25 pencils in 5 boxes 2. 3 fives in fifteen
3. Tom is 10 years old 4. 5 x 4 = 20 sides
5. 5 x 2 x 5 = 50

Pages 46–47 Understanding x6

2 x 6 is the same as 6 + 6 Total = 12
3 x 6 is the same as 6 + 6 + 6 Total = 18
5 x 6 is the same as 6 + 6 + 6 + 6 + 6 Total = 30
6 x 6 is the same as 6 + 6 + 6 + 6 + 6 + 6 Total = 36

Pages 48–49 Six times table

1 x 6 = 6, 2 x 6 = 12, 3 x 6 = 18, 4 x 6 = 24, 5 x 6 = 30,
6 x 6 = 36, 7 x 6 = 42, 8 x 6 = 48, 9 x 6 = 54, 10 x 6 = 60
Missing numbers are: 12, 18, 36, 48, 54, 60

Pages 50–51 Six times table

10 x 6 = sixty
5 x 6 = thirty
3 x 6 = eighteen
8 x 6 = forty-eight
6 x 6 = thirty-six
7 x 6 = forty-two
2 x 6 = twelve
1 x 6 = six

Pages 52–53 Mental maths x6

1. 6 x 2 = 12 windows 2. £6 x 3 = £18 3. 6 x 4 = 24 points
4. 6 x 5 = 30 legs 5. 6 x 2 = 12 centimetres

Answers

Pages 54–55 Understanding x7

2 x 7 is the same as 7 + 7 Total = 14
3 x 7 is the same as 7 + 7 + 7 Total = 21
6 x 7 is the same as 7 + 7 + 7 + 7 + 7 + 7 Total = 42
7 x 7 is the same as 7 + 7 + 7 + 7 + 7 + 7 + 7 Total = 49

Pages 56–57 Seven times table

1 x 7 = 7, 2 x 7 = 14, 3 x 7 = 21, 4 x 7 = 28, 5 x 7 = 35,
6 x 7 = 42, 7 x 7 = 49, 8 x 7 = 56, 9 x 7 = 63, 10 x 7 = 70
Missing numbers are: 7, 14, 35, 42, 56, 70

Pages 58–59 Seven times table

9 x 7 = 63, 1 x 7 = 7,
8 x 7 = 56, 4 x 7 = 28,
5 x 7 = 35, 6 x 7 = 42,
2 x 7 = 14, 10 x 7 = 70,
7 x 7 = 49, 3 x 7 = 21

Pages 60–61 Mental maths x7

1. 14 apples 2. £7 x 5 = £35 3. 7 x 3 = 21 glasses
4. 10 x 7 = 70 years old 5. 7 x 4 = 28 bananas

Pages 62–63 Learn the facts

X	6	7	5
8	48	56	40
3	18	21	15
9	54	63	45

X	6	4	7
5	30	20	35
7	42	28	49
6	36	24	42

Answers that start with 2: 4 x 5 = 20, 6 x 4 = 24, 7 x 4 = 28.
Answers that start with 3: 6 x 6 = 36, 5 x 7 = 35, 6 x 5 = 30.
Answers that start with 4: 7 x 7 = 49, 7 x 6 = 42, 8 x 5 = 40,
9 x 5 = 45, 8 x 6 = 48
The tree on the right has the most kites

Pages 64–65 Learn the facts

4	2	2	1	4
9	5	4	2	1
3	0	7	4	5
6	4	0	2	2
2	5	7	1	8

row 1: 20, 42 row 2: 54, 70
row 3: 14, 12 row 4: 30, 25
row 5: 49, 35 row 6: 36, 60
row 7: 40, 45 row 8: 63

Pages 66–67 Robot revision

8 x 2 = 16, 5 x 5 = 25, 5 x 6 = 30, 4 x 3 = 12, 7 x 3 = 21

Pages 68–69 Understanding x8

2 x 8 is the same as 8 + 8 Total = 16
4 x 8 is the same as 8 + 8 + 8 + 8 Total = 32
6 x 8 is the same as 8 + 8 + 8 + 8 + 8 + 8 Total = 48
7 x 8 is the same as 8 + 8 + 8 + 8 + 8 + 8 + 8 Total = 56

Pages 70–71 Eight times table

1 x 8 = 8, 2 x 8 = 16, 3 x 8 = 24, 4 x 8 = 32, 5 x 8 = 40,
6 x 8 = 48, 7 x 8 = 56, 8 x 8 = 64, 9 x 8 = 72, 10 x 8 = 80
Missing numbers are: 16, 40, 56, 72, 80

Pages 72–73 Eight times table

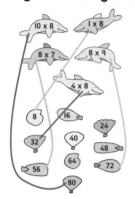

3 x 8 = 24, 8 x 5 = 40,
8 x 6 = 48, 7 x 8 = 56,
9 x 8 = 72, 2 x 8 = 16,
8 x 10 = 80, 8 x 8 = 64,
4 x 8 = 32

Pages 74–75 Mental maths x8

1. 8 x 3 = 24 legs 2. 8 x 2 = 16 sides 3. 4 x 8 or 8 x 4 = 32
4. Five eights make 40 5. 10 x 8 = 80 hours

Pages 76–77 Understanding x9

2 x 9 is the same as 9 + 9 Total = 18
4 x 9 is the same as 9 + 9 + 9 + 9 Total = 36
5 x 9 is the same as 9 + 9 + 9 + 9 + 9 Total = 45
9 x 9 is the same as 9 + 9 + 9 + 9 + 9 + 9 + 9 + 9 + 9
Total = 81

Pages 78–79 Nine times table

1 x 9 = 9, 2 x 9 = 18, 3 x 9 = 27, 4 x 9 = 36, 5 x 9 = 45,
6 x 9 = 54, 7 x 9 = 63, 8 x 9 = 72, 9 x 9 = 81, 10 x 9 = 90
Missing numbers are: 9, 27, 45, 54, 72, 81, 90

Pages 80–81 Nine times table

3 x 9 = 27, 8 x 9 = 72, 2 x 9 = 18, 9 x 9 = 81,
1 x 9 = 9, 6 x 9 = 54, 5 x 9 = 45, 4 x 9 = 36,
7 x 9 = 63, 10 x 9 = 90
The letter A is hidden in the pyramid

Pages 82–83 Mental maths x9

1. 2 x 9 = 18 2. 3 x 9 = 27 3. four nines in thirty-six
4. 5 x 9 or 9 x 5 = 45 5. nine nines in eighty-one

Answers

Pages 84–85 Understanding x10

2 x 10 is the same as 10 + 10 Total = 20
4 x 10 is the same as 10 + 10 + 10 + 10 Total = 40
6 x 10 is the same as 10 + 10 + 10 + 10 + 10 + 10 Total = 60
10 x 10 is the same as
10 + 10 + 10 + 10 + 10 + 10 + 10 + 10 + 10 + 10 Total = 100

Pages 86–87 Ten times table

1 x 10 = 10, 2 x 10 = 20, 3 x 10 = 30, 4 x 10 = 40,
5 x 10 = 50, 6 x 10 = 60, 7 x 10 = 70, 8 x 10 = 80,
9 x 10 = 90, 10 x 10 = 100
Missing numbers are: 10, 30, 40, 70, 90, 100

Pages 88–89 Ten times table

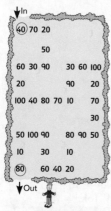

10 x 10 = 100, 9 x 10 = 90,
10 x 6 = 60, 8 x 10 = 80,
7 x 10 = 70, 5 x 10 = 50,
10 x 2 = 20, 10 x 4 = 40,
10 x 3 = 30

Pages 90–91 Mental maths x10

1. 10 x 2 = 20 jellies 2. 3 lengths of tape 3. 10 x 10 = 100
kilos 4. 1 x 10 = 10 hours 5. 5p x 10 = 50p

Pages 92–93 Learn the facts

X	9	10	5
3	27	30	15
7	63	70	35
6	54	60	30

X	6	5	8
9	54	45	72
8	48	40	64
10	60	50	80

x9 Missing 'In' numbers are: 8, 2, 5; missing 'Out' numbers are:
36, 81, 63. x10 Missing 'In' numbers are: 4, 6, 9; missing 'Out'
numbers are: 30, 80, 50

Pages 94–95 Learn the facts

Possible answers are: Across: 1. 10 x 8 3. 2 x 10 4. 6 x 8
5. 9 x 5 7. 10 x 6 9. 2 x 5 10. 8 x 4 12. 10 x 9 13. 3 x 3
or 1 x 9 14. 7 x 8 Down: 1. 9 x 9 2. 9 x 2 or 6 x 3 3. 2 x 1
4. 5 x 8 or 10 x 4 6. 5 x 10 7. 7 x 9 8. 9 x 8 9. 4 x 4 or
8 x 2 10. 3 x 10 11. 6 x 6

Row 1: 36, 45 row 2: 50, 48 row 3: 72, 80 row 4: 18, 30
row 5: 24, 56 row 6: 16, 80 row 7: 54, 81 row 8: 20

Pages 96–97 Looking for patterns

1	2	3	4	5	6	7	8	9	10
11	12	13	14	15	16	17	18	19	20
21	22	23	24	25	26	27	28	29	30

1	2	3	4	5	6	7	8	9	10
11	12	13	14	15	16	17	18	19	20
21	22	23	24	25	26	27	28	29	30
31	32	33	34	35	36	37	38	39	40
41	42	43	44	45	46	47	48	49	50

1	2	3	4	5	6	7	8	9	10
11	12	13	14	15	16	17	18	19	20
21	22	23	24	25	26	27	28	29	30
31	32	33	34	35	36	37	38	39	40
41	42	43	44	45	46	47	48	49	50
51	52	53	54	55	56	57	58	59	60
61	62	63	64	65	66	67	68	69	70
71	72	73	74	75	76	77	78	79	80
81	82	83	84	85	86	87	88	89	90

1	2	3	4	5	6	7	8	9	10
11	12	13	14	15	16	17	18	19	20
21	22	23	24	25	26	27	28	29	30
31	32	33	34	35	36	37	38	39	40
41	42	43	44	45	46	47	48	49	50
51	52	53	54	55	56	57	58	59	60
61	62	63	64	65	66	67	68	69	70
71	72	73	74	75	76	77	78	79	80
81	82	83	84	85	86	87	88	89	90
91	92	93	94	95	96	97	98	99	100

Pages 98–99 Looking for patterns

Missing numbers are: 7: 14, 28, 35, 42, 56, 70.
4: 12, 20, 28, 32, 36. 6: 12, 24, 42, 48, 54, 60. 8: 24, 40,
64, 72, 80. How many: $2 \times 6 = 12$, $4 \times 6 = 24$, $8 \times 6 = 48$

Pages 100–101 All together

Grid one: 3, 6, 9, 12, 15. 4, 8, 12, 16, 20. 5, 10, 15, 20,
25. 6, 12, 18, 24, 30. 7, 14, 21, 28, 35. 8, 16, 24, 32, 40.
9, 18, 27, 36, 45. 10, 20, 30, 40, 50. Grid two: 18, 21, 24,
27, 30. 24, 28, 32, 36, 40. 30, 35, 40, 45, 50. 36, 42, 48,
54, 60. 42, 49, 56, 63, 70. 48, 56, 64, 72, 80. 54, 63, 72,
81, 90. 60, 70, 80, 90, 100.

Pages 102–103 All together

Missing numbers: $4 \times 6 = 24$, $3 \times 8 = 24$, $7 \times 8 = 56$, $7 \times 9 = 63$, $7 \times 6 = 42$, $9 \times 8 = 72$, $8 \times 5 = 40$, $5 \times 7 = 35$. Which is
more: $3 \times 4 = 12$, $9 \times 9 = 81$, $6 \times 6 = 36$, $7 \times 8 = 56$.

Pages 104–105 Be the teacher!

$4 \times 2 = 8$, $2 \times 3 = 6$, $4 \times 3 = 12$, $4 \times 4 = 16$, $5 \times 3 = 15$, $5 \times 4 = 20$, $6 \times 5 = 30$, $3 \times 6 = 18$, $4 \times 6 = 24$, $2 \times 7 = 14$, $7 \times 7 = 49$

Pages 106–107 Multiplication squares

2	x	4	=	8
x		x		x
2	x	1	=	2
=		=		=
4	x	4	=	16

3	x	1	=	3
x		x		x
4	x	2	=	8
=		=		=
12	x	2	=	24

3	x	2	=	6
x		x		x
3	x	1	=	3
=		=		=
9	x	2	=	18

5	x	2	=	10
x		x		x
5	x	1	=	5
=		=		=
25	x	2	=	50

Answers

Pages 108–109 Code breaker

24 M, 14 A, 9 T, 20 H, 16 S, 45 I, 16 S, 14 A, 27 C, 100 E
Secret message: MATHS IS ACE

Pages 110–111 Snakes and ladders

3 x 1 x 2 x 2 = 12. 2 x 2 x 2 x 2 = 16. 5 x 1 x 2 x 5 = 50.
2 x 5 x 1 x 4 = 40. 1 x 3 x 3 x 3 = 27.

Pages 112–113 Table tricks

4, 8, 12, 16, 20, 24, 28, 32, 36, 40

6, 12, 18, 24, 30, 36, 42, 48, 54, 60

8, 16, 24, 32, 40, 48, 56, 64, 72, 80

9, 18, 27, 36, 45, 54, 63, 72, 81, 90

Pages 114–115 Multiplying mates

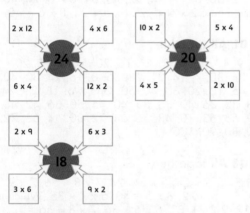

Pages 116–117 Fill the gaps

Possible answers are:
4 x 3 or 3 x 4, 6 x 2 or 2 x 6 = 12
6 x 4 or 4 x 6, 8 x 3 or 3 x 8, 12 x 2 or 2 x 12 = 24
5 x 5 = 25
6 x 5 or 5 x 6, 10 x 3 or 3 x 10 = 30
10 x 5 or 5 x 10 = 50
10 x 8 or 8 x 10 = 80
10 x 10 = 100
Do accept all other correct answers.

Page 120 Sorting hats

8 x 1 = 8, 4 x 4 = 16, 9 x 2 = 18, 5 x 5 = 25

128